By Melissa Lagonegro
Illustrated by Atelier Philippe Harchy

First published by Parragon in 2012
Parragon
Queen Street House
4 Queen Street
Bath BA1 1HE, UK
www.parragon.com

ISBN 978-1-4454-4743-8

Printed in China

A Pet for a Princess

A little story for little learners

Bath · New York · Singapore · Hong Kong · Cologne · Delhi
Melbourne · Amsterdam · Johannesburg · Auckland · Shenzhen

"Poor Jasmine,"
said her father.
"I want to make
you happy."

The next day,
he gave Jasmine
a big gift.
"Open it," he said.

Jasmine pulled off
the red sheet.

It was a tiger cub!

"I will call you Rajah,"
said Jasmine.
She was very happy.

Jasmine and Rajah
did many things
together.

They sat in the sun.

They watched
butterflies.

They played
lots of games.

Jasmine liked
to rub and scratch
his furry belly.
Rajah liked it, too!
Purrrr!

The princess kept Rajah
safe from harm.

And she loved to play
dress-up with him.

Jasmine made Rajah
a cosy little bed.
At night, they fell
fast asleep.

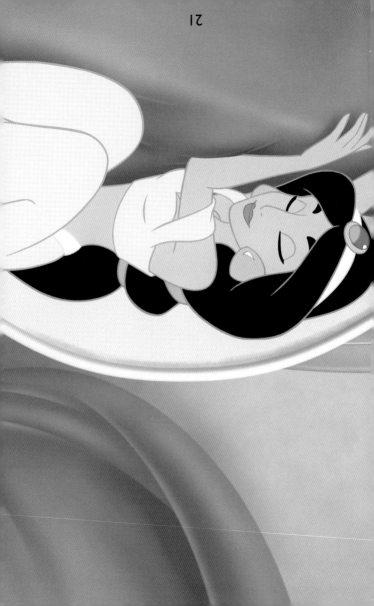

As time passed,

Rajah grew bigger...

and bigger...

...and bigger!

Rajah became
a very big tiger.
And a strong
tiger, too!

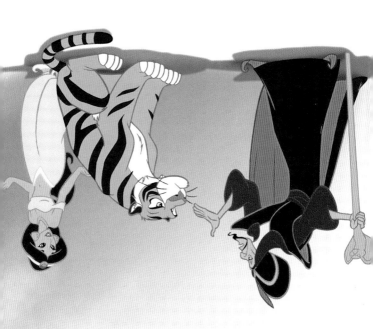

Now Rajah keeps
Jasmine safe
from harm.

Rajah is too big
to play dress-up.

He is too big for
his cosy little bed.

But he will never be
too big for a belly rub…